THE
SEARCH
FOR
ATLANTIS

THE
SEARCH
FOR
ATLANTIS

by Henry Chapin

CROWELL-COLLIER PRESS · NEW YORK
COLLIER-MACMILLAN LIMITED · LONDON

Chapin, Henry.

The search for Atlantis

PICTURE CREDITS

Black Star (Flip Schulke), 95; The Clarendon Press, Oxford (Sir Arthur Evans,
Scripta Minoa, Vol. I), 43; Culver Pictures, Inc., 24; Greek Archaeological
Society, 32–33, 75; Greek National Tourist Office, 18, 50–51, 71; Copyright
Hammond Incorporated, Maplewood, N. J., 28; Historical Pictures Service—
Chicago, 2, 11, 53, 92; Lamont Geological Observatory (Bruce C. Heezen and
Dragoslav Ninkovich, *Santorini Tephra*), 26, 61, 67; Spyridon Marinatos, 32–33,
75; © 1967 by the New York Times Company. Reprinted by permission, 37;
Spanish National Tourist Office, 82–83, 85; United Press International, 57, 58.

CONTENTS

CHRONOLOGY OF THE AEGEAN WORLD

1700 B.C. to 1600 B.C. Middle Minoan.
  Second building of palaces at Knossos
  and Phaistos.

1600 B.C. to 1500 B.C. Late Minoan.
  Cultural interchange with the Greeks commences.

1500 B.C. to 1400 B.C. Late Minoan.
  Greeks invade Crete and take over at Knossos.
  Start of Mycenaean domination of Aegean.

1450 B.C. Knossos destroyed. Crete again isolated from
  Greek world. Squatters take over Minoan palaces.

1300 B.C. End of Mycenaean expansion. Trojan War
  follows.

1200 B.C. Invasions of Greek mainland. Destruction of
  Pylos, Mycenae and other Mycenaean strongholds.
  Followed by times of famine due to progressive climate change.

These dates are approximate but give a progression of
events that seems to be the best present guide for
dating.

1.
Is Atlantis Lost?

The legend of the Lost Atlantis, a beautiful and powerful island kingdom sunk undersea before the dawn of history, somehow refuses to die in men's minds. So many have wanted to believe this legend that numerous books have been written and much research has been done to prove it true. There has never been a stone, a piece of pottery, or an inscription of any kind to prove that Atlantis ever existed except as a necessity of our imagination. Then why do we still try to unravel the mystery? Because a legend like that of Atlantis is necessary to provide the key to solving many unanswered questions about the beginnings of our Western civilization.

The Atlantis legend came down to us through Plato, the Greek writer and poet who lived in the fourth century B.C. Plato himself said that he believed in Atlantis and that the story was passed on to him from a remote ancestor who lived about

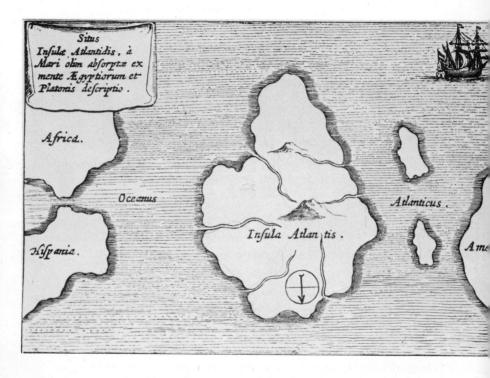

An eighteenth-century Dutch map, based on Plato's description
of Atlantis, shows the "continent" in mid-Atlantic.

600 B.C. This ancestor was a friend of the Greek law-giver Solon, who heard the story from Egyptian priests when he visited the Nile delta. Solon brought back word that Atlantis had existed nine thousand years before his day and was of great size. Plato placed it somewhere in the Greek wild west beyond the Pillars of Hercules at Gibraltar and called it a continent. Today we believe that both these men were wrong in a very interesting way.

Modern Greek scholars say that Plato, and Solon before him, misinterpreted the Egyptian symbol for 100 to mean 1000. Hence their notion of the antiquity and great size of Atlantis. If modern scholars are right, Atlantis was only the size of an Aegean island and met its destruction about nine hundred years before Solon—or around 1450 B.C. At this time a mighty volcanic explosion, which changed the course of history in the eastern Mediterranean, destroyed the island of Thera, or Santorini. Suddenly we have a key to the story that may well prove this legend was based on historical fact. That is the detective story: the probable rediscovery today of the Lost Atlantis in the southern Aegean.

Modern undersea research, through its exploration of the ocean floor along the mid-Atlantic ridge, has proved that it is highly unlikely, if not impossible, for a large island civilization to have sunk beneath the waters between Gibraltar and the Caribbean in the past twenty thousand years. But in finding this out, men have also learned a great deal about themselves and their earlier existence. These findings are all part

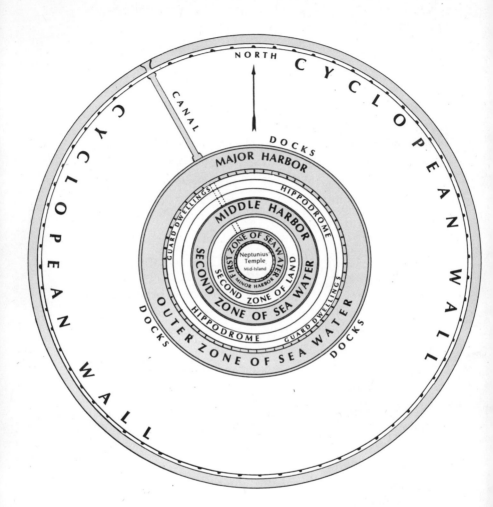

According to Plato, the metropolis of Atlantis was a small,
round island surrounded by circular zones of sea and land.

of the trail that leads our search back into Mediterranean waters.

Plato reported that when Solon went to Egypt the
priests first lectured him on the Greek's lack of interest in their own history and then instructed him.

> *Our histories tell us of a mighty power that*
> *was attacking the whole of the Mediterranean*
> *and even Asia and how you Athenians defeated*
> *the people from Atlantis. The power came from*
> *the ocean where an island stood west of the*
> *Pillars of Hercules. This island was larger than*
> *Libya and Asia and led to other islands in the*
> *west. The island of Atlantis was a great and*
> *wonderful power that ruled over islands and*
> *parts of the continent.*

Plato went on to describe a dream city, an El Dorado befitting the times in which he lived:

> *Atlantis had great stone temples to Poseidon,*
> *God of the Sea, and canals reached from the sea*
> *to a well-fortified inner harbor. The soil was so*
> *fruitful and the rain so regular that there were*
> *two harvests each year when the waters im-*
> *pounded from the rains were used in drier times*
> *for irrigation. The outermost walls of the city*
> *were armored in bronze and tin and orichalcum*
> *[copper].*

Plato ascribed the fall of this rich kingdom into the
sea to Zeus's anger at its citizens because their wealth

had made them greedy and irreligious. And so, with Poseidon's help, earthquake, fire, and volcanic eruption brought everything to destruction. According to Plato, the priests then told Solon:

> *This vast power endeavored to subdue at one blow our country of Egypt and yours of mainland Greece. But your country of Attica shone forth in excellence of her virtue and strength among all mankind; for she was then the first in military skill and leader of the Hellenes.*
>
> *When the rest deserted, being compelled to stand alone, she defeated and triumphed over the invaders and preserved from slavery those not yet subjected and liberated all others who dwelt within the limits of the Pillars of Hercules. But after this there occurred violent earthquakes and floods; and in a single day and night of misfortune all your warlike men in a body sank into the earth, and the island of Atlantis in a like manner disappeared and was sunk beneath the sea.*

When we consider that the island of Thera, or Santorini, blew up about 1450 B.C., probably in a series of explosions, and stopped the clock of history in the Aegean for a century or more, there are three questions to keep in mind: What was it like before this? What were the immediate results? What should we look for today?

To begin, the legend as handed down through Plato needs to be interpreted in a more factual manner. What is told here in simple terms? First, that there was—before the catastrophe or series of disasters—a single great power of high culture and wealth that held subject the Mediterranean peoples from Egypt to the Italian peninsula. There is no statement, except Plato's guess of a far-away Atlantic origin, which indicates whether the center of this island civilization was near the western or eastern end of the sea. Then this strong power suddenly attacked the mainland of Greece after having taken over the outlying areas beyond the control of Attica. This implies an invasion from the Peloponnesus. We know from Plato's report that there were growing upheavals on Atlantis. What could have driven these desperate people to the north except the need to find food, shelter, and a new land in which to live?

But they were not to find this. The Athenians led the Ionian Greeks to victory and a final eruption brought quakes, floods, and a rain of poisonous ash that wiped out the combatants; the island of Atlantis, like Thera, sank beneath the sea.

Although the legend supports the theory that this splendid Atlantean civilization was in all likelihood the recently rediscovered Minoan civilization, more proof is required before we can rescue Atlantis from the storytellers and place it in history as one more revelation such as that of Troy or Knossos or Mycenae or Thebes. This search for further evidence brings us to the remains of the island once called Kalliste or Stronghlie, then Thera and now Santorini—all names for a dangerous volcano that sleeps for centuries as a deceptively quiet island, only to burst apart again and change the face of things. Fortunately, today men can study this treacherous beauty as it lies in a semidormant state above and below the blue waters of the Aegean.

It is possible, of course, that future scientific exploration of the territory in and around Cadiz, the site of ancient Tartessos, may yield convincing proof that here also was an Atlantean stronghold, the western rampart of a widespread culture in the Mediterranean world. When we talk of Atlantis, we are really expressing a belief in a splendid civilization around the inland waters of the Mediterranean that met disaster in the middle of the second millennium B.C. and for many centuries remained unknown to the Greeks and consequently to modern man until the last hundred years.

Professor Anghelos Galanopoulos, the chief seismologist of Greece, became interested in Thera through his studies of the island as a source of earthquakes and volcanic action. He knew of the theories of Professor Spyridon Marinatos and other Greek archaeologists that this island might be the Lost Atlantis described by Plato, and after further research, he became convinced that this was true. With Dr. J. W. Mavor, Jr., of the Woods Hole Oceanographic Institution, he made careful preliminary studies of the island that revealed traces of the circular canal-harbor described by Plato. After taking measurements of the island, he reported that "Santorini (Thera) was just the metropolis of Atlantis, not the whole empire. The empire was said to consist of ten cities. Plato described only the royal city."

The legends that survive do so because we need them to bridge gaps in our own knowledge of things

past. We crave a continuing history of our development as civilized human beings. Often the legends we
cherish are those that prove to have been based on
actual happenings of which no records remained. Oral
reports of things past have turned history into story,
and it is the job of the archaeologist to discover just
how much history these stories contain. That is why
both scholars and romantics have never let the legend
of Atlantis fade from memory.

Attempts to locate Atlantis somewhere under the
Atlantic Ocean have been a kind of wild-goose chase,
but they have increased our knowledge of the sea and
underwater life. Men often do great things and make
unexpected discoveries for completely wrong reasons.
Columbus never believed he had discovered the Western world because, to the day of his death, he held the
fixed idea that he had made a landing in Asia. He
never set foot on the North American continent; his
four voyages were made to the Caribbean. But this in
no way detracts from his bold imaginative search for
a western route to the Orient across a terrifying and
unknown sea.

It is not strange that the early Greeks believed
Atlantis had once existed in the sea to the west. All the
pull of western history has been from East to West.
There beyond the Pillars of Hercules at Gibraltar lay a
vast and mysterious area unknown to the early Greek
world. It was natural to think that the Hesperides, the
Fortunate Isles or whatever men hoped to find, had to
exist in unexplored and unknown seas. It had to be
remote in space as well as time.

But why have serious and instructed scientists been

caught up in this search for a legendary Atlantis? Simply because the magic of the word Atlantis covers a gap in human knowledge and sits at a hub of exploration where many paths lead in. If we find Atlantis, we find an answer to the mysterious voyages of the first Phoenicians beyond Gibraltar. We find the beginnings of a civilization that may have spawned people as diverse as the Mayans of Central America or the ancestors of the Basques who came, they say, from the southwest of Spain and a seacoast community. And where did the Cro-Magnons or the successive waves of marvelously skilled cave dwellers of Spain and southern France come from? Atlantis is a word that covers our lack of true knowledge. Somebody, therefore, has to rediscover Atlantis and maybe come up with all these answers.

As far as climatic conditions go, an island as large as Atlantis was thought to have been could have existed in the mid-Atlantic, or just off Gibraltar, and could have very well enjoyed the perfect climate Plato describes. The slow revolve of the Gulf Stream which, with its sister currents, circles the Atlantic establishes along the east to west path of the north equatorial current a warm and gentle belt of weather under the trade winds that blow from North Africa to the Caribbean. This gentle climate appears to have existed over most of the Atlantic during the third millennium B.C. We also know that the nature of the Gulf Stream is such that even if a great island had stood across its path, it still would have delivered the warm subtropical waters to all the Atlantic.

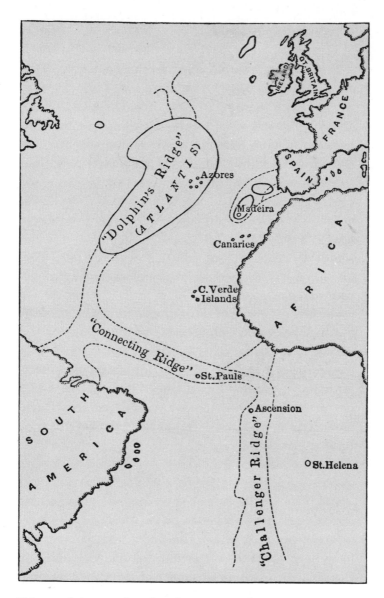

This speculative map, based on deep-sea soundings,
places Atlantis on an underwater chain of islands
bisecting the floor of the Atlantic.

This being so, migrations by sea could have taken place over great stretches of a calmer ocean than we have today. If there had been a chain of islands in the mid-Atlantic, this would have made it still easier. The question of time it might have taken to travel these distances should not bother us. Ancient man was not so obsessed with time as a measure and, therefore, could take months and years to make his move, just as the Polynesian Maoris made their long migration to New Zealand in the Pacific.

Something more than knowledge of favorable conditions is necessary to rediscover Atlantis. But, of course, there are no inscriptions, artifacts, ruins, or any of the usual evidence that archaeologists ordinarily count on in their digging on land. There are certain rumors, however, of past voyaging. The Welsh talk of their drowned city of Llion, the Bretons of the lost kingdom of Lyonesse, and the Irish of St. Brandon's Isle and of Hi-Brazil always west over sea. Oddly enough, in reverse, the Mayans of Yucatan in Mexico have a legend of bearded white men coming to their shores from the east. Thus a starting point for all this— called Atlantis—would be very handy.

But undersea explorers of recent times have come up with nothing to indicate a drowned island civilization in the Atlantic. Many cores of sea-bottom deposits have been taken all up and down the long ridge of higher ocean floor that runs from the Azores south to the equator. The only information of any scientific interest from all this mapping and exploring of the sea bottoms shows that whatever changes of any geological importance may have taken place would have happened long before any civilized existence on a lost Atlantic island were possible.

And yet there is the teasing accumulation of unanswered questions rising from the evidence that tends to show that there did exist, around the north subtropical belt through the Mediterranean basin and westward beyond the Pillars of Hercules, traces of a very early common culture. These trails in various fields of knowledge are like spokes of a wheel visibly sinking underwater to an unknown hub, a sort of psychologically necessary Atlantis. For instance, the blond Guanches, a pre-Spanish race living on the island of Tenerife, practiced mummification of the dead much as the Egyptians did and claimed that their ancestors came from somewhere other than the Canaries.

It is quite likely that in the past there were upheavals and changes in the Atlantic and that mountains and islands rose and fell as the crust of the earth shifted. If there had been an island like Atlantis with bays and streams and shallow waters where eels and salmon once had a permanent home, this might well account for the strange fact that the eels from both European and North American waters swim back to the neighborhood of the central undersea Atlantic ridge near the Sargasso Sea and, deep in this tranquil body of warm water, breed and die. The salmon, likewise coming from this area in the Atlantic, make a reverse journey to their own breeding grounds in the upper reaches of European and North American rivers. Birds have likewise been reported to hesitate and fly about in this same general area on their migrations, as if some instinct still made them seek a long lost home. But again it must be said that this could come from changes long before postglacial times when it would not have been possible for an Atlantean civilization to have existed.

The migration of early peoples into southwestern Europe comes closer to the lost trail we want to pick up. They came in four or more migrations following the retreating ice cap as it moved northward from the Mediterranean area. They were hunters and cave dwellers and primitive according to our standards, whereas the accumulation and care of property and a great desire for a long and sanitary life shape our ambition. Even starting with the Cro-Magnon men, which was at least thirty thousand years ago, we find that these people coming north were not part of a general Aryan migration from the Near East. They had brain pans as big or bigger than modern man, and the testimony of their caves proves them to have been sensitive and expert artists. These people brought spear throwers and flint weapons with them. It is in-teresting that at that early time we find bulls drawn as if they were connected—as in later-day Spain—with some forgotten ceremonies, possibly religious. These people of the Dordogne caves in France also drew pictures of female witches. The spear thrower and female witchcraft are found along the western shores of Africa and in Central America. The usual forms of witchcraft practiced by the Mongolian people of North America, as well as by the Mongols who came into Europe via Thrace and Hungary, was shamanism, or male witchcraft. And this points to a still undetermined point of emigration not only for the Cro-Magnons but later migrations by Solutrians and the most recent of the cave people, the Magdalenians, who arrived from somewhere in the western Mediterranean about 9000 B.C.

One more spoke in the unsolved cultural wheel that could lead to an Atlantis in the west is the practice of the couvade. In this, when a child is born, the father of the family takes to bed and goes through all the mock agony of childbirth and is treated with great care by all concerned. Not so long ago this custom was still practiced in the Basque country between France and Spain and also in North Africa, the Canary Islands, and in Central America. Lewis Spence in his book *The History of Atlantis* puts his case for the lost Utopia in these words:

> *From the shores of western Europe to those of eastern America a certain cultural complex is distributed and is found on intervening insular localities, while its manifestations are also to be discerned in a great measure in North Africa and Egypt on the one hand and in Mexico, Central America and Peru on the other. . . . It is clear now that a lost oceanic link united American and European extremities.*
>
> *The principal elements which distinguish the Atlantean culture complex are the practice of mummification, the practice of witchcraft, the presence of pyramid building, the practice of*

headflattening, the couvade and the use of three pointed stones as markers.

Another savant in such matters, a French professor, M. Termier, has suggested a sensible answer to this rather vague, but fascinating, search: "That there was a cataclysm is undoubted. Did men live who could withstand this and transmit the memory of it? . . . It seems to me that neither geology nor zoology will solve it . . . it is from anthropology, from ethnography and lastly from oceanography, that I wait for the final answer."

What does all this mean in relation to the present transfer of the search for the Lost Atlantis to Mediterranean waters? Simply this, that modern oceanographic exploration of the ocean bottoms has so far come up with no information that would make it likely that within the history of man as a civilized builder of cities there could have existed an island kingdom in the Atlantic Ocean. But modern research has also produced evidence to verify the record of flood, volcanic action, and shifting levels of land along the continental shelf and inland seas to make important land changes there quite possible within the time we shall inspect, from 6000 B.C. to 1000 B.C.

In the Mediterranean basin, which was originally, just after the last glaciation, a great catch basin for the released waters from the ice cap that covered Europe and Russia, overswollen lakes very much like our own Great Lakes cut a way through into the Atlantic. This change of climate and weight of waters naturally affected the sensitive crust of the earth, and the combined release of natural forces changed land and sea and brought similar great adjustments to peoples and their civilizations.

So we stand now in our search for the Lost Atlantis, knowing it is most unlikely that there are lost cities beneath the Atlantic Ocean. Although this search for an Atlantic Atlantis may have failed as archaeology—having produced no ruins, artifacts, stone or bronze records, or even bones—we now know that many questions remain unsolved concerning lively traces of lost civilizations that once existed on the other side of the curtain of history. We see in Spain, in the Libyan Desert, and all along the Mediterranean coasts of North Africa that an intelligent and organized society existed at the time we think Atlantis existed. In other words, the Atlantic search, though wrong, has produced fascinating evidence to place Atlantis and its legend in time this side of 6000 B.C. and inside the anciently known world of the Mediterranean basin.

Thus far we have shown that a legend can contain the material for true historical detective work. This has raised the exciting question of whether or not the Greek island of Thera may really have been the Lost Atlantis. How does this hunt continue? Many things contribute to a final answer. First, we must consider other persistent legends, such as the Homeric stories of Troy and Mycenae, and the faint memories that have come down over the centuries to our own times concerning the kingdom of Minos in Crete before the Greeks had established themselves at the end of the

A view of the island of Santorini from the ancient town of Thera.

Balkan peninsula. These legends have proved true and have yielded to modern archaeological explorations by Heinrich Schleiman and Sir Arthur Evans, and other amateur and professional scholars. Today we can see where Troy once stood, visit the palaces of the great Minoan thalassocracy (the Greek word meaning sea power) in Crete, and the stronghold of Argive Agamemnon at Mycenae. Likewise, in the far north the truth of the Norse and Icelandic explorations to North America—five hundred years before Columbus—is becoming more evident every year.

The modern scientific disciplines of geology, anthropology, oceanography, and meteorology combine to make modern archaeology a truly efficient means of research. When we apply these studies by new electronic devices to the Mediterranean, Atlantis draws nearer, and we see it as a possible part of the great Minoan world of the second millennium B.C.

The scholars give us the first clue, and then the oceanographers and other scientists carry the actual search not only undersea but literally under the floor of the seas.

Beginning with Tartessos near the site of the present Spanish city of Cadiz, we shall pursue the trail of Atlantis eastward to the Aegean. From there we shall center home on the latest discoveries at Thera, the volcanic island that blew up about 1450 B.C. and changed the face of things from the Peloponnesus to Egypt and Palestine, causing famine and migrations during the so-called dark ages of Greek history.

2.

The Curtain of Time

Legends belong to prehistory, a land of guess and discovery that hovers on the far fringe of historical time. There is always the continuing effort to unravel legend and myth to find out what historical truth lies hidden in them. And every now and then the curtain of time shifts and reveals hidden meanings—things once thought of as inventions come out of the dark into the light. The detective work of bringing the past into the present view helps us, who are alive today, to see ourselves in time as travelers in a continuing stream of life when we recognize the people of the past as part of ourselves. We discover that people as human beings change very little. And we try to find out who were these people of Atlantis, what were the circumstances of their lives, and just where was this mysterious island.

Modern research, while it takes legends and attaches them to historical fact, does not destroy the value of the legend. On the contrary, it affirms the capacity of mankind without any written aid, century after century, to hand down history in the guise of storytelling with an accuracy that few men have been willing to believe.

Before the modern end of this venture into our past can be told, it is first necessary to glance at our customary idea of time and the character of these cultures that were well developed without the use of the written word. Time is not watches, trains, planes, and factory whistles only, any more than a blizzard of paper and the printed word is more true or accurate than carefully memorized reports by trained and responsible ancient poets and bards.

On the radio or television today we often hear the announcer say that part of the program is "live" and part recorded; it is often difficult to tell which is which. We accept the modern tape recording as fact. The legends and sagas that men told and retold in ancient times and kept as accurate as possible were the recordings they used to recall their history as a tribe or family. A televised football game, even if we see it a year after it was played, has all the reality of the moment. So the legends of the old-time poets seemed to the listeners hungry for human news and excitements. They were accepted as true and stirred men then as now with a sense of reality.

It is the task of the prehistorian to make ancient times as immediate as the present. They have to deal with·two kinds of time: the marking-off of years, centuries, and millenniums in what we call chronological time, named after Cronos the father of the Greek gods; and another kind of time that deals in the reality of feelings and not of numbers. Clocks tick, speedometers say sixty miles an hour, calendars pace off the days. But we also speak of the time of our life, classical times, of a time for weeping or a time for joy, and other qualitative phrases coming from the measure of our sense of emotional recognition. This has little to do with chronological time. Myths and legends tried to bridge this difference between the two kinds of time. They placed man at the center of the world of *Now* that is fed by both past events and future imaginations.

To make history live we must think of ourselves at the center and hub of a great wheel of life. We stand at *Now*. Some spokes bring in reports from the very beginnings of our history. We use this report to fashion our lives from experience and project our future actions with these real images (the act of imagination) and a spoke goes out from our center into the future. Other spokes bring in the immediate reports of only yesterday. All these passing through ourselves at the hub and center of our minds make up our feeling of reality. History is not a junk shop of facts stored in the attic. It is the report of living experience from the lives of many men dead and gone that help us face the living moment.

Legends and sagas are not mere fancies to amuse idle people. They represent the remembered voice of people who once lived and died in the midst of great events with as much reality and excitement as we wish our own lives to have. Because the listeners yearned for the true story of the past, they have always been severe critics of the tales the bards and poets recited about their ancestors. The Norse sagas came down to us after two hundred years of oral recitation before they were written. But modern scholarship, in cross-checking the stories and working out the details of their voyages in discovering North America in A.D. 1000, has found these sagas for the most part to be historically accurate.

During the past hundred years the same kind of revelation has been made about the much older legends and stories of the very beginnings of our Western civilization in the Near East. The Deluge at the time of Noah has become an archaeological reality. The location of Troy and the Homeric story of the Trojan War has changed from legend to historical fact. The lost ancient civilizations of Crete, and of Mycenae on main- ↓ land Greece, have emerged from legend to visible cities and beautiful works of art unearthed from mere piles of rubble by Schleiman and Evans and others who believed that persistent legends meant what they said and could be proved historically true.

What we call prehistory is a modern outgrowth of archaeology—a pursuit that isn't very old itself. Only in the last hundred years has archaeology come to be a careful and scientific study of ancient times. Before that we had collectors of art objects and artifacts and mere treasure hunters of buried valuables. All this has now turned into a method of historical research. Prehistory takes archaeology beyond the discovery and classification of things and applies these data to the interpretation of how men used to live. It is primarily interested in what we call cultures. Because of this many new and hitherto unused methods of detection have been

The Norse sagas about Viking voyages to North America have been shown to be historically accurate for the most part.

brought into use to widen all fields of interpretation. It is a kind of frontier detective story sifting fact from fancy and determining what is honest and believable in the legends and other ancient reports. The early Greeks, for instance, had no historical documents, no comparative material, no archaeological experience, no records. The past was legendary or unknown.

Prehistory deals with Man rather than men. It is anonymous because it deals with unwritten sources such as oral legend. It uses many methods of scientific detection of given conditions at certain times to piece together how men lived and enjoyed themselves in the past. It tries to steer clear of making guesses about their ideas. Yet prehistory broadens and deepens the whole frontier of historical research. The simple collecting and classification of artifacts in time does not go far enough.

Here are some of the methods used to clear up the half-known of prehistoric culture in order to enrich our historical knowledge. At one time, when there was a legend that might locate a suspected site of an ancient city, men could start careful excavations, hoping one day to hit the jackpot. Today air photography helps to define changes in the earth we do not notice on foot. We can preserve corroded metals and rotten wood that might otherwise disappear in today's fresh air. We can even analyze the contents of a mummified stomach, tell (by the use of carbon 14) the relative time that a piece of bone or wood was burned, and discover the kinds of pollen that have survived time and thus indicate weather and climate. With our new undersea diving equipment we can search out lost cities under the

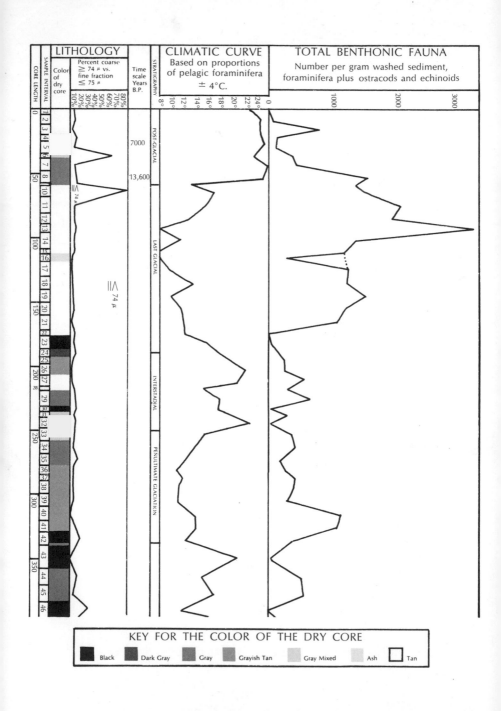

LITHOLOGY

Color of dry core

Percent coarse ≧ 74 μ vs. fine fraction ≦ 75 μ

80% 70% 60% 50% 40% 30% 20% 10%

≦ 74 μ

≦ 74 μ

CORE LENGTH

SAMPLE INTERVAL

Time scale Years B.P.

7000

13,600

CLIMATIC CURVE
Based on proportions of pelagic foraminifera
± 4°C.

STRATIGRAPHY

POST-GLACIAL

LAST GLACIAL

INTERSTADIAL

PENULTIMATE GLACIATION

8° 10° 12° 14° 16° 18° 20° 22° 24°

TOTAL BENTHONIC FAUNA
Number per gram washed sediment, foraminifera plus ostracods and echinoids

0 1000 2000 3000

KEY FOR THE COLOR OF THE DRY CORE

Black   Dark Gray   Gray   Grayish Tan   Gray Mixed   Ash   Tan sea, the wrecks of ancient vessels, and the patterns of sea trade. Thus geology, geography, seismology, anthropology, chemistry, and other apparently differing disciplines of discovery are brought together in the great detective study we call prehistory.

When all the data is more or less scientifically collected then trouble can begin, because it is the nature of men to differ and argue in the face of so-called facts, and it is particularly the nature of academically trained scholars to do so. Therefore we have theories of interpretation at headquarters after the detective force has brought in the evidence.

To take an example, until quite recently the most popular theory about the spread of culture in our Western world started with the Egyptian and the Sumerian as the oldest of our highly developed cultures. All Mediterranean culture was presumed to have spread and diffused from this center, and even the earlier interpretations of American Indian culture was, by these particular believers, supposed to have Egyptian influences. Recently, although diffusion of cultures is an obvious fact, other theories have naturally developed as research methods advanced. Now we see that under similar circumstances spontaneous inventions and discoveries of ways of living can come into existence. Sometime before 3000 B.C. rice culture developed in China, wheat and barley culture in Asia Minor and the

A chart based on a core sample taken west of Crete. Note the ash layer indicating volcanic action 25,000 years ago.

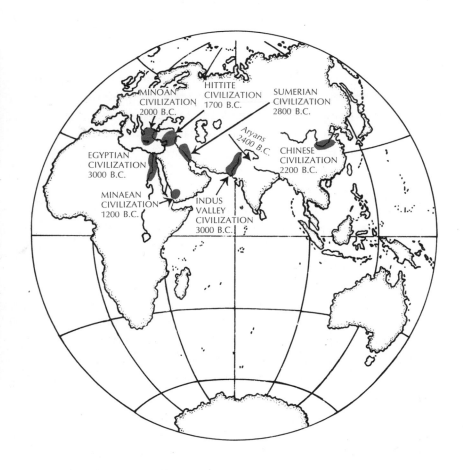

Many civilizations flourished between 3000 and 1000 B.C.

Mesopotamian valley, and maize or Indian corn culture in the Americas. Men thus advanced in prosperity, and different inventions developed in the different cultures. The wheel was unknown, for instance, in the Western hemisphere until introduced by the Spanish only a few hundred years ago. There is also another factor, which we will take up later, and that is the effect of sudden catastrophe on blotting out advances in culture and perhaps even changing or controlling the nature of man himself.

It is easy to see that the role of the prehistory explorer into man's past is not a simple one. But if we concentrate on the Mediterranean world, and begin with the changes and development of that world from about 6000 B.C. to 500 B.C., this will avoid a certain amount of controversial discussion. After all, we are on the trail of a single legendary culture, the Lost Atlantis. This requires joining several methods of detection into a simplified picture that will help us place this legend in history. So we must push back up the stream of Mediterranean history to the limits of prehistory and begin in the year 6000 B.C. with the geography, agriculture, and migration of peoples caused by a series of great natural catastrophes that drove eastern inland tribes from their former homes to the edge of the Aegean Gulf of the Mediterranean and from there out upon the sea to the great island of Crete and the lesser islands of the Aegean.

3.
Land and Sea

Man started to become a domesticated animal and to domesticate the lesser dumb animals and to grow his food about 10,000 B.C., which was just after the last retreat of the glacial ice from Europe and Asia. Why then and not earlier or later? To answer this we must put prehistory on the map and find out what change in living conditions permitted this sudden jump in methods and inventions. This development changed man from the hunter to man the artisan, a person who applied artificial controls to wild nature and thus started our present civilization.

Students of the earliest beginnings have been so busy digging, dusting off, and measuring that the scholars now believe man, as the kind of animal we are today, began existing on earth at least six hundred thousand years ago. Shrink all those years to an hour composed of sixty minutes and we can measure the beginnings of civilization as starting one minute ago. That means fifty-nine minutes of that hour measure were taken up by savage man as hunter and food gatherer. Late Stone Age man or Neolithic man is the subject of prehistory. We can trace him by cave drawings and by finding his weapons and primitive dwelling places. Civilized man belongs only to the last half-minute of that hour measure when, about five or six thousand years B.C., he came out of the East and began to take over the Mediterranean world. The strange behavior of the earth itself had a lot to do with this.

At first the slow retreat and then the increasingly rapid melting of the last ice cap in Europe and Russia greatly affected the more southern lands. Stamp the earth and it seems solid, but the crust is elastic, and although it takes its own time, it lifts and falls with the weight of shifting waters. When this water is locked up, say, as the ice of a great glacial field to the north, not only are the southern seas drained of their natural supply of water but a great additional weight is pressing down upon the dry lands. When the glaciers melt, as they did more than ten thousand years ago, which in geological time is recent, then the weight on the earth slowly shifts back to the seas. The water level rises, and whole peoples find themselves in trouble.

The stories of the Flood are reports of real catastrophes. We are most familiar with the tale of Noah and the Ark, but the Sumerians have the story of Gilgamesh, the East Indians have a similar story of a great flood as do the Chinese, and the Greeks the legend of Deucalion. After all these natural upheavals, people migrate and renew their place on earth.

The legend of Atlantis is little different from these

An ancient Minoan site is buried beneath these vineyards.
(Photograph courtesy of the Boston Museum of Fine Arts.)

stories. It is placed on an island, and the immediate cause of its destruction is largely volcanic. But earthquakes with accompanying tidal waves and the eruption of volcanoes all go together and are often triggered into action by greater, long-term changes, such as the shifts of earth and climate caused by the increasingly rapid retreat of an ice cap. Because of this we can close in on the time in prehistory when it was most likely that Atlantis flourished and came to sudden destruction. This would be, if its location was in the eastern Mediterranean, somewhere between 6000 B.C. and 1000 B.C., when the peoples of Asia Minor for various reasons—such as floods or great droughts—moved to the seacoasts and occupied the islands of the Aegean. Just before these years, the two great inland seas that originally composed the Mediterranean basin filled up from the overflowing waters of the Black Sea and the run-off of the melting glaciation. A land bridge that had existed from Africa to Italy via Sicily gave way as did a similar obstruction at Gibraltar. A new way of travel with fresh incentives to exploration opened from Syria to the Pillars of Hercules. Cyprus, Crete, and the islands of the Aegean became inhabited and, because of their isolation from attack, strong and relatively safe civilizations flourished in these new lands. The water level of the Mediterranean basin in 3000 B.C. was probably thirty feet higher than ever before.

After the years of greatest change, the river valley civilizations were the first to develop—first the Sumerian on the Euphrates and soon thereafter the Egyptian dynasty along the Nile delta.

The weather over Europe and the Mediterranean

basin had settled into a climate that was better bal-
anced and with more normal rainfall than today. The
period from 4000 B.C. to 1200 B.C. was a good one for
people to develop the arts of living in settled communities. Pottery, the use of the wheel, the plow, and other
great advances developed and spread from Mesopotamia to the then fertile lands of northern Africa. The
coastal desert did not then exist in Libya and in the
lands west to the Atlas Mountains.

Great droughts hastened the movement of people
from Asia Minor in 3500 B.C. and about a thousand
years later in 2200 B.C. At this time the first small cities
were built along eastern Crete, and by the third millennium, when the second migration began, the powerful
Minoan civilization came into existence at Kato Zakro,
Mallia, Phaistos, and Knossos. We know that these cities
developed a high culture and enjoyed a peaceful rule
of the Aegean and the waters of the eastern Mediterranean. At that time there was no danger of strong pi-
ratical sea raiders. Small vessels hugged the coast and
dared not put to sea by night or during the winter season. This would have also applied to the mythical island
of Atlantis, which is described by Solon as free from
attack by either land or sea. Other than Crete itself, the
possible sites for an existing Atlantis during those fortunate centuries would have been the southern Aegean
islands or coastal communities on safe peninsulas of
sea-encompassed land, perhaps at the western end of
the Mediterranean. We know that there were such well-
established civilizations by 2000 B.C. in Libya and along
the African coast as far as Tartessos in southern Spain
just beyond the Straits of Gibraltar. There are cave

drawings in the Sahara Desert of cattle and shepherd's dogs and horse-drawn chariots, where today only camels exist.

The change of climate is part of the machinery of our developing civilization. The aftermath of the last glaciation had a great deal to do with the kind of weather that permitted man to settle down from hunting and wandering and to build his great cities. Men were learning the uses of copper and how to alloy it with tin for bronze weapons. The ice lock-up to the north, along with its aftereffects, was definitely over, and the weather was almost like today's but with less extremes of dry and wet. The healthy stimulus of a temperate storm belt came through the Mediterranean world. Two thousand years later this had moved north to European lands with its energizing weather.

As Atlantis is described in the legend the Greeks brought home from Egypt, it stood on a great round island well to sea with, weather permitting, two crops a year and where the arts of life, much similar to those of the Minoan civilization in Crete, were well developed. No natural enemies could reach Atlantis in any force across the sea. In the second millennium B.C., which is a little earlier than the time Homer depicts in the *Odyssey*, only stray adventurers accomplished long journeys and then seldom across open water. It was considered a bold feat for Agamemnon to cut across the northern Aegean from Troy to the opposite shores of Thessaly. There was no compass, no good rudders, no maps.

The people of Crete, and the adjoining islands of the

The first map, of the Aegean, shows Santorini (cross) north of Crete. Atlantis may have lain in the area enclosed by the dotted line in the detail map, with the center, sacred island on Nea Kameni, a growing, volcanic island today.

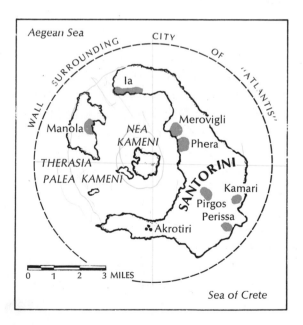

Aegean a hundred miles to the north, probably came there by way of Cyprus, Rhodes, Karpathos, and then the eastern tip of the great island itself. The first settlements were at Kato Zakro and then Phaistos and Mallia and, finally, the greatest of them all, Knossos, where the modern city of Herakleion now stands. These cities were tied both to the northeastern culture of North Syria through trade with Ugarit and Biblos and were also connected with the southern Nile culture of Egypt. It is also possible that there were trade connections and an exchange of trade goods with the Libyans of North Africa to the south and west.

But because a great catastrophe intervened between Cretan culture and the islands of the north, very little is known of the connections with the larger islands such as Thera, which lies seventy miles to the north and at that time was a solid, well-harbored, round island presumably inhabited by a people not much different from the Minoans. Except for accidentally burned clay records found in the storage jars of Knossos and the pottery and stone fragments that a great catastrophe left behind, only the legend of Atlantis hints of this sister civilization that must have existed about the time the palace dynasty of the Minoans flourished between 2500 B.C. and 1500 B.C.

The catastrophe that cuts off this part of prehistory from present knowledge was not another great flood such as we read about in the Asiatic legends. It was a time of great earthquakes and sudden volcanic action that changed the face of the eastern Mediterranean world. Atlantis lies somewhere just the other side of this curtain of fire, tornadoes, ash, and racing tidal wave, that is, if it exists in reality and not as a fairy tale concocted by Plato.

We are beginning to have factual reports on the study of this moment of the earth's upheaval due to modern studies of the sea bottom around Thera and the study of the effects of massive volcanic action as observed at Krakatao in Indonesia as recently as 1883. These awful explosions, which killed thousands of people and wiped out hundreds of sea-coast towns in a few hours, are not unlike the description of the destruction of the legendary Atlantis. As we know, such a cataclysm blew up the whole island of Stronghlie, called Thera by the ancient Greeks and now called Santorini. We also can, and will, trace the effects of this upheaval for hundreds of miles throughout the eastern Mediterranean.

This great volcanic upheaval just preceded a second natural factor that is one of the causes of the so-called dark ages in early Greek history. Shortly after the destruction of Minoan cities, the Mycenaean culture on the Greek mainland reached its peak and began to decline. The war against Troy may well have been a last desperate effort to search out new sources of food and fish from the straits leading into the Black Sea. This was precipitated by a definite change in weather conditions throughout the Mediterranean that caused a discontinuity in Aegean civilization for almost four hundred years and all memory of Atlantis, except for legend, was lost until the present day.

For a long time archaeologists have tried to explain the lack of progress in pottery and other signs of civilization as due to a great horde of people called Dorians who flooded down from the north and destroyed everything Mycenaean that they could lay their hands on. There is very little evidence to support this. The more likely reason for this gap in historical and cultural progress was the onset of dry weather and the consequent build-up of the Sahara south of the Mediterrenean.

Recent studies in Africa show that Libya was once rich in cattle and that chariot routes ran from Tripoli on the Mediterranean to Lake Chad and Timbuctoo. Geologists tell us that a cycle of dry weather every eighteen hundred years caused widespread droughts and hence migrations of people throughout the Near East. We have records of such devastating droughts about the year 3000 B.C. and the beginnings of another at the end of the second millennium B.C. In the past two thousand years, fluctuations of twenty feet in the level of the Mediterranean Sea can be measured. The level is higher now than in ancient days.

Other records show that the great Hittite Empire in Asia Minor collapsed about 1200 B.C.; Egyptian records relate that the "people of the shores and isles," meaning the Greeks, were restless and loose of foot in those times and attacked the Egyptian delta. All this, according to Dr. Rhys Carpenter, emphasizes natural forces and volcanic disaster, plus protracted drought and the enforced migrations of Aegean and Balkan peoples, as the real reason for the blank in historical progress from 1400 B.C. to 900 B.C.

This drought was brought on by the trade winds of summer that began to blow—as they do today—dry and continuously down the Aegean for many months of the year. For some reason the normal storm belt that brought rain in from the Atlantic moved north beyond the Alps. It was several centuries before this condition improved, and it has never regained the balance of climate that apparently existed before 1200 B.C. Thus, it was much more likely the upheaval of Thera, followed by a progressive and radical worsening of Mediterranean climate, that caused the sudden end of the Minoan, Mycenean, Hittite, and other powerful early civilizations than the unproved guess that huge hordes of destructive Dorians stopped all Aegean development dead in its tracks for three or four hundred years. It was not the Dorians who pulled down this curtain in time between the Greek world we know and their forefathers, but rather great natural catastrophes.

It is now time to put together what we do know of that splendid age that existed around Crete and Thera in fifteenth century B.C. just before the great explosion.

4.
The Aegean World
of 1500 B.C.

By now in the search for the Lost Atlantis, we know we have to have what is called an optimum time and place for such a civilization to have flourished. There is such a time and place. This lucky circumstance was due to the settling down of the wild natural forces let loose by the retreat of the glacial ice fields in the far north. After 3000 B.C. the Mediterranean basin enjoyed a fine climate of adequate rainfall more temperature than today. Also, it was virgin territory for enterprising peoples to start fresh and build in lands where there were few natural enemies and the fruits of the earth abounded. The vine, the olive, and domesticated animals came into the Mediterranean with migrating peoples who knew the wheel, the chariot, the art of pottery and weaving, and how to make weapons of bronze. Their ships were adequate for voyages from isle to isle. Luckily, there were few long stretches of open sea to hinder exploration or trade.

This was indeed the opportunity for something like

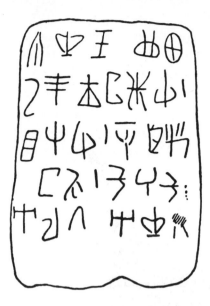

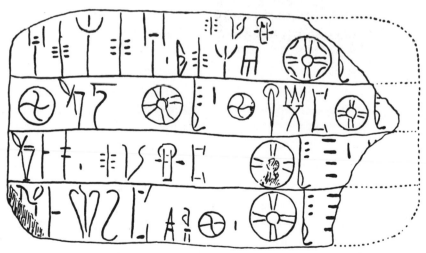

Tablets from Knossos showing the Linear A (above) and Linear B (below) scripts.

a golden age in human development to take place. It began in the river valleys of Mesopotamia and on the Nile and found safe refuge in the islands, particularly in Crete. For tens of centuries whatever we know of these people today was buried in mystery and only reported by legend, myth, and story. They were a verbal people whose inscribed language, which we call Linear B, was used largely for keeping accounts. And it is modern archaeology and scholarly studies of old legends that have combined to bring some of their magnificent world into view. But so far it has only been a start on greater matters. The Linear A alphabet of the Minoans has yet to be deciphered. For every ancient burying ground or sunken merchant ship or city that has already been excavated, as much or more still remains to be uncovered. The sea itself has secrets to give up that only in the most recent years have come within the reach and eye of man.

But what we now know is enough to encourage us to renew our search for an actual Lost Atlantis. It must have flourished in what we call the Neothermal period after 3000 B.C. This means the beneficent, new warm period. The violent flooding and consequent fluctuations of sea level had become stabilized. The shepherd tribesmen of the Fertile Crescent, which curves from northern Palestine eastward around the northern limits of the Arabian Desert, had combined in their new city civilizations the metallurgy of the mountains and the domestication of cereals and beasts. The decorative arts naturally began to flourish because of the prosperous times. Then in Asia Minor came a great season or seasons of drought, the fall of kingdoms and the migration of civilized people into virgin lands, people who often forgot their own history and started new phases of culture, such as the Greek tribes of Asia Minor and the Etio-Cretans, who probably came to that large island from North Africa. This is where our search has come, as that island civilization taking on fresh migrations from Syria and the east grew mightily in power and in civil arts because it was free of envious neighbors. The Cretans were never a military people, although they no doubt had the most powerful navy in the Aegean for hundreds of years.

So the Minoans, from the eastern city of Kato Zakro and Phaistos to the south, traded with Ugarit and Biblos and the Egyptian Nile. Others from Knossos, with its seaports, began to search out trade routes in the west, and we find Minoan pottery and bronze weapons as far distant as southern France and the Po Valley in Italy and at Tartessos, between modern Cadiz and Seville. Even the Mother Goddess of the Near East came to rest in Crete, though she changed her names from Ma and Cybele to Dicte. Because of this migration from the dry inland areas in the second millennium B.C., three new centers of power developed in the eastern Mediterranean. They were Syria, Egypt, and Crete. The first two were subject to conquest, while Crete stood safely remote in the sea. But the power centers remained whether the Hittites or Assyrians held the Palestinian seaports, or some fresh dynasty took over in Egypt.

Nature was the most feared enemy of the Minoans. They worshiped a bull-god, the Minotaur, who lived in labyrinthine caverns and roared as their earth roared at the time of the frequent earthquakes. There was a devastating catastrophe at Knossos in 2100 B.C. Every few hundred years more walls came tumbling down, but each time the palaces of the kings rose again and prosperity resumed, until in fifteen hundred B.C., the Minoan kingdom was at its peak, together with Thera and other Aegean islands allied to it.

A thing to keep in mind about this prosperous and relatively undisturbed period of Mediterranean, and particularly Aegean, expansion in the middle of the second millennium B.C. is that we know much more about it today than did the Greeks of Plato's time. They were neither historians nor archaeologists. They held to their great legends of the past, but their attention was the troubled present. Plato, who was an unhappy aristocrat living in a warlike and demagogic age, used his imagination to create legend and explore the abstract nature of the kind of world in which he wanted to live. It was a strictly disciplined and idealistic republic and had little to do with the Athens of his day, and it certainly was merely guesswork when he talked about Atlantis.

But this much the legend did tell. There was a great sea power that controlled countries from Egypt and Libya to the toe of Italy and eastward to Asia Minor. The center of this kingdom was an island with a rich plain surrounded by a circular canal or canals, inner and outer, with safe harbors. In those days, the legend said, hostile ships and voyages were not heard of and the people were safe from attack. Poseidon and Atlas were the gods of this people.

Poseidon and Atlas were African and Libyan gods as well as, later on, Greek gods. It is important to remember that the Greeks we read about from Homer to Pericles were newcomers to the Aegean as compared to the Minoans. To them affairs beyond the dark ages, which were a curtain of ignorance that separated them from the Minoans, were matters of legend. From 1200 B.C. to the end of the nineteenth century A.D.—about three thousand years—no factual knowledge of the great Minoan-Mycenaean civilizations existed.

And if Plato were here today we could tell him this. Yes, your Great-grandfather Dropidas was right in reporting what his friend Solon told him. There was a mighty power in the Mediterranean world existing beyond the dark ages, and it did come to a sudden end in a series of great catastrophes. After these great disasters its people, fleeing to the Greek mainland, came to grips with the early men of Attica and were defeated, while their island home disappeared beneath the sea in a great volcanic explosion.

But before this happened this splendid civilization of Atlantis, or something so much like it that we are ready to believe it was the same, had many centuries of good life in the southern Aegean on the island of Crete and the other islands, such as Thera, or Santorini, to use its modern name. Like your Atlanteans, these people built an orderly and beautiful society under kings called Minos. They erected splendid palaces, lived well from the rich central plains of their island, and built ships that coasted along the shores of the Mediterranean as far as Spain and northern Italy, where they made contact with traders come down the Rhone Valley or through the Brenner Pass from Denmark with tin and amber. These same merchants penetrated the length of the Black Sea and likewise traded with Syria and Egypt. Then in a few brief years this civilization collapsed, unable to renew its strength or to extend its culture.

Imagine, for a moment, the experience of being captain of a merchant ship from Amnisos, the port for Knossos, returning with tin and amber from the far west beyond Italy, where he had traded fine bronze weapons and Eastern goods from Asia. This east-west reach up and down the Mediterranean was not too difficult because the winds from the north or west filled the square sails, giving a rest from the oars.

But the captain was uneasy as he came by Stromboli and Etna in Sicily for those volcanoes were more than usually active. Some of the towns he stopped at for food and fresh water reported recent earthquakes and small tidal waves. These things were constantly in the minds of the Minoans familiar with the awesome rumble and tremor of the earth on their own great island of Crete. Approaching Cytheria off the southern Peloponnesus, the air was heavy and the men had to take to the oars. The captain did not like these signs. He made for a small harbor under Cape Malea, beached his ship, and made camp for the night on a hill where he could watch for possible marauders and study the sea and the signs of weather. Pirates wouldn't bother a Cretan vessel for fear of reprisal, as the Minoans and their Mycenaean partners, who by now shared control of western Crete, held all the Aegean in fee.

For this reason a Cretan sea captain had little fear of being attacked or murdered by the people of the Peloponnesus, for they, like himself in the mid-1500's, were safe within the double control of a Mycenaean power from the mainland and the Greek-Minoan kings that now held power at Knossos.

That night of vigil on Cape Malea passed with no danger other than a minor tidal wave that just failed to wreck his craft in its little harbor. This was a customary hazard of those times in the southern Aegean. The next day a fair norther sped his forty-foot double-ender around Cytheria eastward and south to his home country. To the northeast he could see the high, round dome of Thera riding peacefully with its fine city and circular harbors against the bright horizon. Neither he nor anyone else then knew that this great, round island, called a stronghlie, was a dormant volcano that thousands of years before had suddenly blown itself to pieces. Now it was long rebuilt, up from the sea bottom, and subject only to the intermittent earthquakes that all felt in that area.

Although this Cretan merchant had his home port at Amnisos, he could likewise coast east all along the northern shores—first to Mallia and thence passing the great bay we call Mirabella, around the eastern end of Crete by the fine princely city of Kato Zakro, and thence, perhaps with a load of cedar from the mountains, to Phaistos on the south. Here he could exchange goods with Libyan vessels and perhaps an occasional Egyptian merchant, though that trade had fallen off of late.

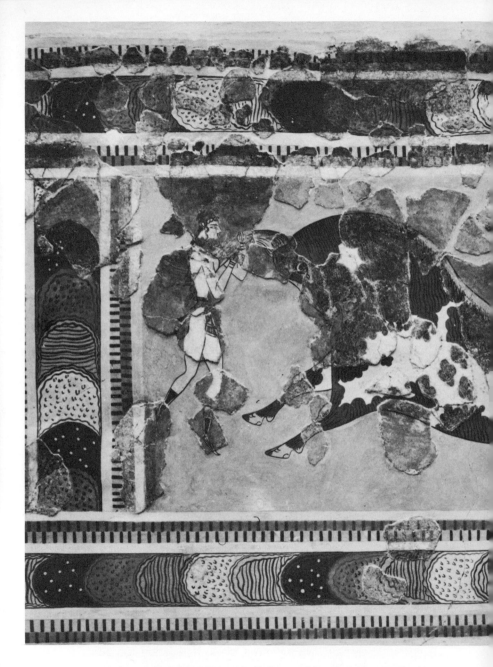

A fresco depicting Minoan bull-dancers from the palace at Knossos.

He was lucky to be a citizen of this Minoan-Mycenaean civilization of the federated Cretan cities. No military service was required of him, and times were very good indeed. Back at Knossos there was a succession of games and bull-dancers performing in the great megaron of the palace; the portside was alive with Mediterranean gossip and many men from all points of the Aegean world. No one could challenge his freedom or the freedom of his wife as Cretan subjects. At that time women were not considered inferiors in the Eastern world. This was a world of artists and merchants before the matriarchal world had been reshaped into a more masculine and militant society.

Although it is just to speak of the fifteenth century B.C. as a kind of golden age when the commerce and art of the eastern Mediterranean world flourished, food was plentiful, and the climate was in the final phase of its mild and well-watered Atlantean period, there were plentiful signs of trouble underfoot. But prosperous people do not like to think that their own times will not last forever. The Cretans and their neighbors made sacrifice to the rumblings of the bull-god who shook the earth, and cast offerings to Poseidon who suddenly sent tidal waves against their shores. Aside from these warnings the sea level had stabilized after rising three feet a century since the melting of the glaciers in 10,000 B.C.

At this time Egypt was at the height of her power and held lands in fee from Babylon to the Upper Nile. The Jews were captive slaves along the delta. To the west

A Minoan goddess from Crete, dressed in court costume and holding the sacred snakes.

the long plains of the African sea coast, held by the Libyans, were fertile, and five hundred miles inland, in the hills around Tassili olive and cypress grew. The Egyptian raiders came back from Libya with grain and cattle. Only the first signs of a drying-up had started and were scarcely noticeable. Beautiful cave drawings have recently been discovered at Tassili that give testimony to a rich and long-established succession of African cultures.

But Crete and her sister islands, such as Thera, lay beyond the reach of conquest, although it is evident that there had been a strong exchange and infiltration between the Minoan and Mycenaean cultures in this fifteenth century. The cities prospered, but the people perpetually made offerings to the strange threat of natural forces. The remains of the great city of Kato Zakro show this. Perhaps those more aware of the repeated warnings from the shaking earth had already moved on. Cadmus may have been one of these foresighted leaders, leaving Thera and coming up the Peloponnesus into Boeotia and settling Thebes about 1500 B.C.

Meanwhile the palace life at Knossos went on apace. A gay and prosperous society developed there as a center of imperial wealth. Women under a matriarchal goddess lived free and open lives in no way subordinate to men. Copper for the aristocratic classes came in from Cyprus, tin from Tartessos in the far west, amber from the European traders coming over the Alps, and gold from the Numidians of the Upper Nile. The olive and the vines, along with sheep and goats, were all domesticated to island use, and the forest still stood dark and tall upon the mountains.

But nature had not finished the transition from an ice age that once had lowered the sea more than three hundred feet and established a crushing weight of ice over the lands beyond the Mediterranean world to the north. In terms of geological changes, it took a very short time for this ice cap to melt, to form great terminal lakes, and then to have this mighty weight of waters cut south and west to form the Mediterranean Sea as we have known it since 3000 B.C. There was and still is today to a lesser degree, a final adjustment to this change. The elastic surface of our earth was stretching and shuddering to adjust to these new tensions, and man, whose time sense is measured to his own life span, could not foresee the image of things to come.

It is true that in almost every century there had been fierce recurring earthshocks and tidal waves in the east, and on occasion volcanoes had burst their bounds and brought fire and destruction. But men forget and cannot live in fear, and the world of the Minoan and Mycenaean people in the fifteenth century B.C. could not guess the extent of the catastrophe that drew nearer.

5.

The Explosion of Thera

Probably the thirty thousand or more inhabitants of Thera, and those of other islands in the south Aegean Sea, were so accustomed to earthquakes and occasional tidal waves that they were little prepared for the great and final catastrophe. They had no newspapers to keep them in a state of worry, and they could say prayers, burn goat's meat on altars, and throw wine casks into the sea to keep Poseidon happy. And then one day in spring or summer—we know this by the direction of the winds—literally all hell broke loose, and a civilized, well-inhabited island disappeared in fire and smoke, leaving a great hole, or caldera, that sucked in the surrounding seas.

First, a strictly factual scientific description of what we have discovered must be recorded. In a map the island is situated halfway between Athens and Crete. But a modern map does not show how it looked in 1450 B.C. It was a round island with harbors on a circum-

A volcanic eruption on the island of Santorini killed
fifty persons in 1926.

Afterwards, men gathered to investigate the rock-strewn
scene of the eruption.

ference formed by canals, inside an outer reef of islets, which marked the rim of an ancient crater. This crater had gradually rebuilt the island over thousands of years (by the second millennium B.C.) from an open caldera full of water—an undersea crater—to a once more habitable island. There had been a great blow-up about twenty thousand years before, but nobody knew that. This island was a vent for relieving the slowly accumulated pressures along an unstable seam in the earth's crust that runs through the Gulf of Corinth southeasterly to Crete and thence branches into Asia Minor and continues southerly down the Red Sea and the Great African Rift.

We know best what happened by comparing what modern man observed in the great explosion of the island of Krakatao, in 1883, in the Sundra Straits between Java and Sumatra. This explosion of an island horrified the world. Forty thousand people lost their lives, hundreds of villages were destroyed, and the effects of the eruption were felt thousands of miles away in tidal waves and clouds of ash, and even the roar was heard two thousand miles to the west in Ceylon.

From studies made by Dr. Dragoslav Ninkovich and Dr. Bruce Heezen of the Lamont Geological Observatory of Columbia University, we can now estimate that the eruption of Thera was four to five times as great as that of Krakatao. Here are the kind of facts. Scientists have long been interested in discovering what natural phenomena might have caused the halt in civilized development in the Aegean area between 1300 B.C. and

900 B.C., the so-called dark ages. They were not satis-
fied with the rather glib suggestion of some historians
and archaeologists that crude tribesmen called Dorians
poured down from the Balkans and were alone responsible for destroying a strong and magnificent Minoan-
Mycenaean culture.

Using modern means of undersea exploration, team
work between geologists, seismologists, and meteorolo-
gists—students of the earth's crust, of earth shocks, and
of the weather—has opened up new horizons for the
pursuit of archaeology. In 1947 a Swedish expedition to
the eastern Mediterranean took deep cores of the sediments of the sea bottom and studied their composition.
This is very much like reading a column of ancient history, in terms of the sequence of inscriptions laid down
by nature.

This led to further study of the sea bottoms and to
the certain knowledge, by placing and dating layers of
volcanic ash called *tephra*, that there had been a great
natural catastrophe just about the time we knew, from
our legends and bits of history, that there had been
widespread destruction and a halt in the advance of
civilization in the Aegean and around its borders. The
Vema of the Lamont Geological Observatory made several cruises in the late 1950's, and from the cores then
taken it has been possible to map out the extent of the
blow-up of Thera and with the use of carbon 14 to
show an approximate date for this explosion, which fits
in with the land discoveries of various archaeologists.

As the map plainly shows, this most recent field of

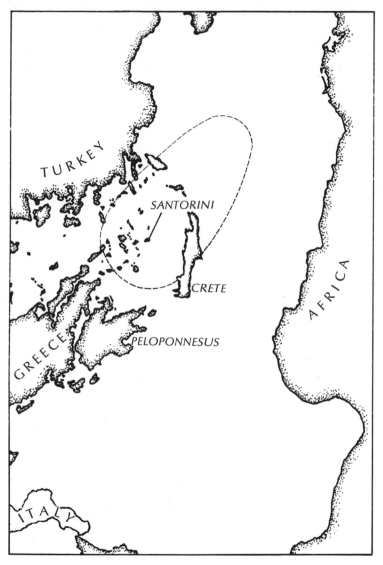

The enclosed area on this map shows the extensive distribution
of tephra as revealed in core samples taken by the
Lamont Geological Observatory.

ash, or *tephra*, extended seven hundred kilometers southeast of Thera, and covered an oval-shaped area of about two hundred thousand square kilometers. This varied in thickness from a deposit of thirty meters thick on the island itself to a few centimeters at its greatest reach. Being caught by the sea, it could slowly sift to the bottom and leave a map for us to dig up. This ash mixed with water forms a pumice stone that we often find on land. There, of course, the wash of rain and the shift of winds does not leave us the convenient pattern that we find undersea.

It is necessary to study the force of an explosion that could have laid down such a pattern of devastation. No combination of atomic bombs yet exploded on earth can compare in energy with the eruption of Thera. The whole top of the island disappeared in fire and smoke, leaving a great hole a thousand feet deep and acres in extent into which the sea rushed adding to the clouds of steam and ash that filled the skies of the eastern Mediterranean. Winds of hurricane force and a succession of violent lightning storms reached beyond the fall-out of the ash. They carried damage and destruction as far as Egypt and eastern Libya and extended northward to include most of the Cyclades. It has been estimated that the sound of this thunderous explosion must have been heard as far west as Gibraltar and northward into middle Europe.

Naturally enough, the nearer lands of the Eastern ancient world were overcome by the holocaust that was reported in the Old Testament and in Egyptian writings.

There is no written Greek record, just silence and a blank in any ancient knowledge of what went on. What we know today is due to the combined efforts of archaeologists and other scientific explorers. From this we now see that the wrecked cities and palaces of Crete and Asia Minor and the numberless small towns and villages of the Aegean disappeared almost overnight, while devastating earth shocks and other types of disaster fell upon the civilization of the Egyptian delta along the Nile.

We are more familiar with the biblical description of the plagues that struck down Egypt at the time of the Exodus of the enslaved Jews—the floods, the whirlwinds, the falling of stones and fire from the sky, the rain of blood that made red the rivers. We know that the Jews escaped and fled east and that they could cross the receding waters of the Red Sea before their pursuers, who arrived as the waters came rushing back upon them. All these phenomena are the inevitable accompaniment of such a disaster as that of Thera. Great tidal waves rushed across the sea backing-up rivers and flooding shores. Showers of sand and stone carried high by the hurricane gales fell upon the land, and the vast quantities of oxidized iron sulphide turned red and stained the torrential rains the color of blood. All this was accompanied by the distant roaring of the explosions at Thera, as well as by the noise of continuing local earthquakes brought on by the general disruption.

The memory of the Exodus is vivid. The sixtieth Psalm records: "Thou hast shown the people hard things;

Thou hast made us drink the wine of astonishment."
And in the eighteenth Psalm: "Smoke . . . and fire . . .
and coals were kindled. The channels of the water were
seen, and the foundations of the world were discovered." And as for Mt. Sinai in the desert east of Egypt,
which indeed may have been the cloud by day and the
pillar of fire by night, it is reported in Judges: "The
earth trembled . . . the mountains melted . . . even that
of Sinai."

From Egypt there is also what seems to be a firsthand
report of the great catastrophe in a text known as the
Ipuwer Papyrus. It reads not unlike the Jewish Lamenta-
tions.

The land turns around as does a potter's wheel.
The towns are destroyed. Upper Egypt has be-
come a waste. All is ruin. There is no end to the
noise. Plague is throughout the land and the
river is blood. The hail smote every herb of the
field and broke every tree of the field. There re-
mains no green thing throughout all the land of
Egypt and the gates and the columns and walls
are consumed by fire and there is thick darkness
in all the land of Egypt.

This is the report from Egypt. We can imagine what
happened in Crete halfway between Thera and Africa,
where the middle and eastern part of that great island
lay in the path of the death-dealing gales. If we take the
modern reports from the Krakatao disaster, and mul-
tiply their effect, that should give us a reasonable

facsimile of what happened over a period of many days when the lovely stronghlie of Thera disappeared in a final eruption and left a great chasm that drank in the sea. The huge *tsunami,* or tidal waves, racing at more than two hundred miles an hour, first created the withdrawal of waters from a shoreline and then a towering onrush that flooded inland and knocked flat all shipping and housing along the coast. These waves would have inundated Egyptian coasts and Tunisian shorelines, run at terrific speeds to the coast of Israel, and no doubt made themselves felt as far as Gibraltar. Two hours after the explosion the eastern Mediterranean shores would have been hit.

So much for the immediate effect of the final outburst. Darkness must have covered the skies for a week, while ash sifted over the ruined cities and the blasted crop lands. In the face of a succession of tidal waves at least sixty feet in height very little of the shipping in the Aegean or the waters to the south and east could have survived, to say nothing of the seaports built along the shores. The poisonous gasses destroyed the fertility of the soil and fire swept the villages and palaces alike. That is why we hear in the Jewish reports that the first-born of the Egyptians were slain in a night. By first-born they mean the high-born, or palace dwellers. There, as in Crete, the aristocrats in their stonehouses suddenly struck by an earthquake suffered more in proportion than the slaves and laborers in their mud and wattle dwellings, which surely burned but did not fall in and crush them. That is why revolt follows such disaster and terminates the hegemony of one culture while another lower group slowly rebuilds and takes over. This seems to have happened in Crete, just as there was also a revolt of the Helots in Sparta after that city was wrecked by a quake in 464 B.C.

The accompanying maps of the shift in power of the Minoan-Mycenaean thalassocracy after mid-fifteenth century B.C. looks as if it were part of the explosion itself. The fine cities of Knossos, Tylissos, Mallia, Gournia, Kato Zakro, and Phaistos were no longer the centers of a peaceful and magnificent culture. Slowly, there was to be some rebuilding and a secondary flare-up of Minoan art, but the power that once ruled the thalassocracy of the Aegean was broken. The refugees first moved to the relatively untouched western end of Crete and migrated from there, some to the Peloponnesus or even Boeotia, and others from the eastern towns to the land of Canaan, where we later find them as Philistines. After 1300 B.C. Crete gradually disappeared into limbo as a distant land of pirates and had little or no influence on the later upsurge of Greek culture in either the Aegean-Ionian cities or on the Greek mainland.

All we have of this time is the legend of the Lost Atlantis, a lost civilization and culture very much like that suddenly destroyed in Crete and at Thera. Plato, having placed this legend in the unknown and far-away Atlantic of his day, has not made it easy for the explorers of prehistory to bring back the search to the home grounds of the Aegean.

Although most signs at present seem to point to the

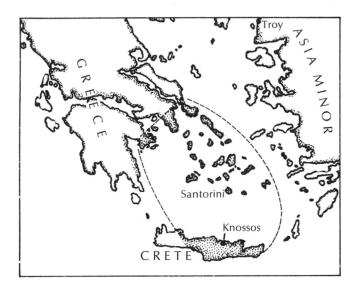

Map A shows Minoan civilization from Neolithic times
to 1400 B.C.; Map B, Mycenaean civilization after 1400 B.C.
to 1180 B.C., when Troy fell.

Aegean as the ancient site of an Atlantean civilization and to Thera as the likely metropolis of part of this civilization, which closely resembles the description in Plato's legend, there are still other possible candidates. Plato wrote that this Atlantean world the other side of the so-called dark ages had ten or a dozen large cities in its widespread thalassocracy. But what about the great western port of Tartessos and its mines and trading fleets that were supposed to dominate the western Mediterranean?

6.

The Aftermath

Modern scientific methods of underground and undersea exploration, combined with a study of the early
records by scholars, today for the first time present a
believable picture of the Aegean world just after the
devastating blow-up at Thera. A civilization called Minoan by Sir Arthur Evans, who first revealed its magnifi-
cence at Knossos, had flourished and grown in com-
mercial power and artistic merit for a thousand years.
At the time of its destruction, it had reached a peak of
peaceful growth and was joined in a cultural exchange
and possibly a joint political control, not yet defined,
with the great Mycenaean civilization on the Greek
mainland.

Although it is necessary to use fixed names for these
ancient people, such as Minoan, Mycenaean, Achaean,
Dorian, Ionian, and so on, to describe those living in
different localities, it is well to remember that this is
somewhat a matter of convenience and intelligent

guess. We do not know what the people of the kings called Minos called themselves. We have no exact record of Ionians or Dorians or Pelasgians, in the modern sense, organizing and conquering any area at a specific period.

We know that many tribes made successive migrations from the Near East down the Balkans to the tip of Greece or across the Aegean, island-hopping as far as Crete and the Cyclades. Certain strains of people dominated this migration at different times and gave it a name. It is much like speaking of the Anglo-Saxon conquest of the American continent. Many nationals, many religions, and many social classes composed this migration, and so we call this mass movement of North European Protestants "Anglo-Saxon" only as a convenient term.

The explosion of Thera created widespread conditions of famine and destruction, which caused a fresh Aegean shifting around of peoples and centers of power, and was so devastating that for many years not too much that was new or fresh went on in Aegean culture. Thus we have what our lack of knowledge forces us to call a dark age. Today we are on the edge of dispelling much of this darkness, and Thera is the focal point of the search.

We know the Aegean and North African coasts enjoyed a better climate and were more fertile and much less bleak in the fifteenth century B.C. than they are today. We also know something of the nature of the central explosion that overwhelmed much of this area.

The harbor of Santorini today.

It was like nothing that had happened before in the memory of mankind. The fertility of the lands as far as Egypt was blasted overnight by gas and fire and a blanket of poisonous ash. Earthquakes shook stone dwellings into rubble, and the seaports and harbors were crushed with racing walls of giant tidal waves—not one but many—and authority of the government went out of the land.

We know that for a hundred years no strong central government in the various areas of Crete and the Cyclades could be reestablished. We also know that in Egypt a change of governments suddenly occurred and that the conquests of Thutmose III came to an end. Pharaoh Amenhotep made no real effort to defend himself against the Hittite invasions from Asia Minor, but tried instead to maintain friendly relations with his neighbors. He was followed by the religious Iknaton. Egypt was a hundred years rebuilding its inner strength after the plagues of destruction caused by Thera, when the records report that "confusion seized the eyes and there was no exit from the palaces for nine days of violence and tempest and neither gods nor men could see the face of their fellows."

The second area of disruption started at Crete and spread west and north in a series of refugee migrations that penetrated beyond the isthmus of Corinth to the rich plains between Thebes and Orchomenus in Boeotia. Here the legend of Cadmus begins to come to life. No one can speak of specific dates at this time, and our approximation may be off by fifty years or so, but this makes little difference as to what happened. A King

Cadmus was supposed to have come from Phoenicia to the island of Thera, and thence migrated in the fifteenth century B.C. to Thebes, which is northwest of Athens, where he set up a powerful city and eventually built, after the Cretan pattern, a great palace that has been called the Cadmean. This was legend until the mid-twentieth century A.D.

This is what happened. Men digging a deep cellar hole for a new building in the sleepy, little provincial market town of modern Thebes came upon great slabs of hewn stone and walled treasure rooms. In every direction the signs of an extensive Mycenaean type of palace structure disappeared deep under the streets of Thebes. Here at last in fact was the true Cadmean that legend had reported. Here was one more indication that the things men persist in memorizing usually have an indestructible base of fact beneath the overlay of fable and fantasy.

Jars were found in the few rooms opened by the digging of this cellar hole and in them were small jewels, carved stone roller seals from Syria, gold from Afghanistan, and amber from the Baltic. Inscribed tablets in both Linear A and Linear B—the scripts used in both Minoan and Mycenaean bookkeeping—were also found. But there are other similar types of writing on clay that have not yet been deciphered, and these far-away artifacts in Boeotia may in time help decipher scripts from Crete and possibly Tuscany that so far have defied the experts. The most interesting thing about the nature of the finds, small as they are, is the fact that many of the seals and some of the jewelry is of foreign origin, which adds to the evidence of widespread trade and migrations of groups of people at the time of the great eruption. So the story of Cadmus, son of the Phoenician king, coming to the beautiful island of Thera—then called Kalliste, meaning the best—and thence being ordered by Apollo to come to the Greek mainland, seems to be one more legend turning into newly revealed fact.

There were other migrations from the destroyed lands that have been revealed to us on a more factual basis. The most recently uncovered remains of a fine trading city called Kato Zakro, on the Eastern end of Crete, tell us two things. They show the size and wealth of the Minoan confederacy of towns that composed the thalassocracy of the fifteenth century B.C., and they indicate that the trade connection with Cyprus and the Near East was a lively one. No doubt the people from Kato Zakro were the escaping ones who came into the land of Canaan about that time and were known to the Jews as the Philistines. The other important fact that has been dug up at Kato Zakro is evidence that the widespread destruction at Knossos and Phaistos and other Cretan cities all came about suddenly and at a single time.

The date for the building of the palace is the important contribution from the recent excavations at Kato Zakro, which prove, too, the sudden destruction of the city. The prosperity of Kato Zakro coincides with the general prosperity of Crete in the fifteenth century B.C. Its destruction, measured by carbon 14 analysis of the ashes and study of artifacts found in the ruins, coin-

Archaeologists excavated these whole jars, lying in a crowded storeroom. The pressure of volcanic pumice and ash has cracked them like melons.
(*Photograph courtesy of the Boston Museum of Fine Arts.*)

cides with the general destruction caused by Thera at the end of that century.

It is too simple to say that all this happened as a stroke of fate with no warning. There are general signs of earlier alarms—minor earthquakes and remains of offerings to the gods to stave off further trouble. But people never willingly leave their homes except under the intolerable conditions of political or physical disaster. No doubt there were minor migrations from Crete and the islands of the Aegean before the final eruption of Thera, but not enough to disrupt the prosperity of those good times. From Knossos trade routes spread south and east to the various seaports; overseas trade to Asia Minor, and west and north to southern Europe, further increased the prosperity of the island.

Then suddenly there was a complete break. Little trading went on after 1400 B.C. No new developments in art and pottery. No immediate rebuilding of the stricken palaces. To the generation of the great eruption it truly seemed like the end of the world, as even the far-away records in Egypt and the Holy Land testify. A look at the two maps on page 67 showing the culture displacement before and after the disintegration of Thera gives a clearer picture than words. It looks as if the Minoan-Mycenaean civilization had been bodily exported northeast to the Greek mainland, and as we read in Homer, revived there as the Mycenaean power under kings like Agamemnon and Nestor and the wily Ulysses.

It is well to remember that until modern times the famous stories of Homer in the *Iliad* and the *Odyssey* were almost all we knew of this period. And even here the scholars debated with each other over whether two different men wrote these stories and, again, whether their descriptions of the heroic Greek age really presented a picture of the thirteenth and fourteenth centuries of Mycenaean times, or, on the other hand, were descriptions taken from nearer Homer's own time, about the eighth century B.C., and transferred to these stories of the ancient Greeks.

One interesting point can be made for Homer. In the *Iliad* there is a list of the kings and their soldiers and sailors and ships that came to do battle at Troy sometime in the late thirteen hundreds, when Troy fell and the way to the Dardenelles and the trade of the Black Sea was thrown open to the Aegean Greeks. In this listing of the allies Homer mentions King Idomeneus of Crete with eighty black-prowed vessels. This would indicate that by then some considerable strength had returned to the kingdom of Minos under the Mycenaeans, and it also indicates that there must have been general accord between Crete and the great Mycenaean power in Greece.

This is backed up by recent studies of the clay tablets found all over Crete and on the mainland at Tiryns, Mycenae, Pylos, and Thebes. These tablets are inscribed in Linear B, which was primarily used for keeping accounts of arms and supplies at the various palaces. It is an old Greek script, deciphered not too long ago by a scholar, Michael Ventriss. Here at last was additional proof for the thesis that just before the explosion at Thera, and afterward when Knossos was rebuilt, Mycenaean power from the mainland controlled the lands of King Minos.

This evidence has been the subject of heated controversy among scholars and has no place here, but is mentioned because it illustrates how a combination of methods of search can explain things hitherto dark to us. The study of pieces of pottery and styles of art alone cannot give a true reading of historical happenings, because very often political and military conquests and change of rule can occur without any real change in a culture. Lower cultures often take on the pattern of those they conquer.

Our exploration of the effects of Thera on the early history of Greek culture would be incomplete without some mention of the Dorians. Schoolbooks tell us that the Ionians, except for those in a few places such as Athens and the Ionian coast of Asia Minor, were conquered by the Dorians and that the great Mycenaean civilization fell before the armies of men with iron swords and that the bronze age came to a sudden halt.

This Dorian invasion, though in the main real enough to describe a conquest from the north and east, has been used too frequently to cover up our ignorance of the real reasons for historical changes in the early Greek world of the Aegean. Archaeologists have been very slow to admit that a great natural catastrophe happened about 1450 B.C. It has been easier to attribute the sudden fall of palaces and change of rule to a vague, but mighty, army of fierce men with iron swords who everywhere and at once burned down the beautiful palaces and conquered the land of Greece and Crete.

Surely there was invasion. Probably, like most invasions, in waves of conquest over a considerable period of years. Surely those people from the north, or more likely from Asia Minor, brought different gods and new forms of witchcraft and somewhat different ways of life. But modern investigation is now pointing-up the fact that the catastrophe of the great eruption of Thera initiated the collapse of the Minoan civilization, which also collapsed on the mainland when the Mycenaean cities were attacked and looted shortly after the time of the Fall of Troy.

As we begin to unravel this background of happenings in the Aegean, it points up the importance of the present attempt to discover what happened at Thera in that terrible hour when the world seemed to be coming to an end in the Aegean of the fifteenth century B.C. A look at the simplified timetable or chronology of events in Crete, mainland Greece, and Egypt shows roughly what is known of the emergence of history from prehistory in the second millennium B.C. New methods of study with recently developed means of undersea and underground measurements can resolve many doubts and bring us closer to the roots of our own Western civilization.

This search goes on not only at Thera but up and down the length of the Mediterranean, for the Atlantean civilization our legend hints at was widespread and composed of many cities not yet discovered.

No one knows how far back in time the rumor of the West teased the minds of the Mediterranean and, later, the people of western Europe. The Greeks dreamed of the Hesperides with its golden apples and the Fortunate

Isles somewhere beyond the Pillars of Hercules. The Spaniards had their El Dorado, and the Celts and the Icelanders were likewise haunted by the west-walking path of the sun. It was natural enough for a Greek poet like Plato to plant his own Atlantis in the Ocean of Atlas, just as Homer, representing the first explorations of the earlier Asiatic Greeks, told of voyages beyond the setting of the sun. So the Phoenicians and the Phocians and others of the Near Eastern lands talked of a mythical kingdom just beyond Gibraltar called Tartessos.

Tartessos did exist. Its name is like many of the names from Asia Minor that we find spread among Greek peoples. It is not a classical Greek name but from earlier sources, just as are names like Peloponnesus, Halicarnassus, and Parnassus. This leads people to believe that there was a very early Mediterranean trading connection between the eastern and western ends of the long inland sea. It also leads to the belief that perhaps the kingdom of Tartessos was really the Lost Atlantis that men still look for. Its capital could have been at the site of modern Cadiz, which anciently was a small island.

And we also move our search to the coasts of Atlantic Spain that stretch from Lusitania, now Portugal, to inside the straits as far as the present Malaga. Seville is supposed to have been the inland capital of Tartessos and the little silted-up port of Niebla on the Rio Tinto near Jerez is thought to have been the seaport where the great trading center of Tartessos once existed. We first hear of this in the Old Testament when King Solomon traded with Hiram, the Phoenician king of Tyre

and Sidon, for gold and apes and ivory brought from
Tarshish. We read in Herodotus of a man called Colaeos
of Samos who made a voyage to Tartessos and returned
laden with a great fortune in silver. Then, of course, the
story of Plato, without naming Tartessos, places Atlantis not too far away. An earlier Greek colonial poet,
Stesichorus of Himera in Sicily, in the eighth century
B.C. wrote a long poem about Geryon the king of an
ancient land beyond the Pillars of Hercules, and spoke
of Arganthonius the silver king and how the city of
Tartessos was "rooted in silver." For this country is rich
in many metals and particularly in tin, which the people
of the bronze age needed so much for their weapons
and utensils. In the Roman times a writer called Avenius
said of Tartessos: "Its wealth is spoken of as silver but
for its real nature there might be said to be a mountain
of tin." He located this in the Sierra Morena near the
Portuguese border.

Tartessos is not quite the mysterious place that Plato's
Atlantis is. We know there was such an area at the
western limits of the Greek world. We also know that
it was beyond Gibraltar facing the Atlantic, that it was
rich in metals, and that its vessels traded north and
south and reexported rare ivory and fish from African
shores and traded in amber and tin from the far north.
We learn much of this through the Phoenicians. These
magnificent sea-tramps finally took over Tartessos
about 500 B.C. and thereafter controlled the western
trade in and out of the Mediterranean gates.

Before that time Tartessos was a strong country noted

Tartessos may have lain near this Spanish beach
in the province of Cadiz.

for its wealth in minerals and also as a source for bronze and bronze age weapons for export. In fact, when the Babylonian king Nebuchadnezzar destroyed Tyre, the Phoenician home port in 574 B.C., Arganthonius, the king of Tartessos, shortly after attacked and for a time held the Phoenician colony of Gades on its rocky peninsula. Carthage, however, soon came to the rescue, and we hear no more of the ancient and mighty Tartessos after 500 B.C.

The legend and fact of our knowledge of Tartessos goes back long before the Greeks and Phoenicians broke through at Gibraltar. It goes back about six thousand years to the migration of the last cave painters from North Africa, who were known as the Magdalenians. It was natural that this area was one of the pathways for people fleeing from North Africa from either drought, pressure of war, or overpopulation. Sea charts today show depths of only about thirty fathoms for most of the way across the narrow straits. We know that there was a land bridge from England to the Continent as late as 3000 B.C. before the final inroad of the North Sea. It could well be that as late as this the channel between Africa and Europe at Gibraltar was almost closed and easy to pass over. This would also hold for the shallow straits between Sicily via Malta to the Libyan coasts. The third millennium B.C. marked the first eastern explorations that we know of into the Mediterranean. The valley civilizations of Sumer and Egypt were already in existence.

Atlas was a north African god and the mountains of

West of Gibraltar lies the Spanish port of Huelva,
from which Columbus set sail.

Morocco bear his name. Hercules was a relative of Atlas and also an ancient god of the Libyans; he was called another name by the Phoenicians before the Greeks transformed him into a sort of Paul Bunyan bully-boy. Poseidon, the sea god, was also held in high esteem in the western Mediterranean long before the Greeks of Attica paid homage to him. A goddess very much like Athena, called Nieth, was a patron of Tartessos. The Tartessians were a people of the sea who held lands not only rich in minerals but with fine, well-watered pastures, and the Greeks had their myth of Hercules stealing the cattle of Geryon. Geryon was a god of the Tartessians and before that was supposed to have migrated with the White Berbers to Spain from North Africa.

What does all this prove about the Lost Atlantis? It established in legend that there was a connection between the earliest Greek culture and the western Mediterranean. Beyond this, the names Atlantis and Atlantic come from North Africa—territories with which the Greek traders were familiar. In addition, the earliest Greek poets, such as Homer and Stesichorus, both wrote of the far Hesperides or the lands of Tartessos, just as in the days of Solomon the Phoenicians of Tyre and Sidon traded with Tarshish in the far west. The ancient walled seaport of Tartessos was doubtless a place not unlike that described in Plato's myth.

Certain Spanish and English archaeologists believe that Tartessos had two capitals, one at Seville and the other at Niebla at the head of navigation on the Rio Tinto. They also think that this was the site of the ancient Atlantis, because it fits Plato's story of a rich, peace-loving, sea-going people whose city was suddenly destroyed by an earthquake and a great flooding of the seas. According to a legend from this area: "The waters rose up from below and the sea came out of its center." Could this have been around 1450 B.C., when vast earthquakes and tidal waves ranged the length of the Mediterranean world? As yet not enough excavation has been done in this area to confirm this, although a great field for archaeological exploration lies there. But a start has been made and it does raise very interesting questions.

Not even the most optimistic archaeologist today expects to find a bronze plaque inscribed with dates and names saying *This is Atlantis*. A more complicated detective story is involved. It starts with the known fact that there was a great sea-trading city of Tartessos, capital of a kingdom by that name. We know it flourished beyond Gibraltar on the Atlantic before the time of the Greek and Phoenician kingdoms. It was a city famous for its mineral wealth, its bold navigators, and its peace-loving people. We are looking for its exact location today between Gibraltar and the Portuguese border. The most likely findings come from Niebla on the Rio Tinto just west of where the Guadalquivir River comes down to the sea from Seville.

The pioneer work in exploring the site of Niebla was done some years ago by Mrs. E. M. Whishaw, an English woman well-informed in archaeology. She worked in cooperation with noted Spanish archaeologists. In 1930 Mrs. Wishaw published a book called *Atlantis in Andalusia*. At the same time she established a small museum at Niebla that contains many of the prehistoric finds made in that area and at nearby towns, such as Sanlucar and other sites in the province of Cadiz.

One thing is certain, the town of Niebla was once a rich seaport at the head of tidewater, although it is now much silted up. The walls and an ancient structure called the Queens Tower stand above an old disembarking pool connected by a long flight of steps. Conduits for bringing fresh water from across the head of the pool can still be found and, in fact, the modern town draws its water from this source. The cyclopean structure of huge, finely fitted masonry and the use of a packed lime and earth artificial-stone known as *hormigón* point to builders who worked many hundreds of years B.C. The old workings at the Rio Tinto mines, which are still in operation today, also show remains of stone age engineering of a superior type.

Around this site and as far east as Cadiz a number of early artifacts have been collected, including beautifully wrought jewelry and signet rings that predate the Greeks and Phoenicians.

What kind of people could have been involved in this prehistoric civilization? From studies in comparative alphabets, the use of flints, spear throwers, and the organization of a strong matriarchal society and other ways of life, it seems likely that the original settlers and builders of the kingdom of Tartessos were White Berbers from Libya and the Atlas Mountains who had crossed at Gibraltar. There is no doubt that other migrants and adventurers, including the early Greeks, came through there and were absorbed into the society.

The earliest statues reflect the archaic smile familiar to us in the ancient finds from Libya and the Aegean.

It is interesting that six meters deep under Seville itself city excavations have brought to light a sort of labyrinthine sun temple, perhaps once the ancient Tarshish of the kingdom of Arganthonious. The masonry is similar to that at Niebla and the vaulting and style of bricks in the chambers is definitely neolithic. There still exist ancient pillars in Seville called, for want of a better name, the Pillars of Hercules.

The facts so far known establish knowledge of a flourishing prehistoric sea kingdom near the mouth of the Guadalquivir with a strong inland river port at Seville. This kingdom had outlying trade and fishing colonies along the African (then Moratanian) and Portuguese (then Lusitanian) coasts. The mines of the Rio Tinto brought great wealth to this kingdom and drew traders from all along the Mediterranean and possibly from as far north as the tin mines of Cornwall. When the Phoenicians took over at Cadiz, they destroyed Niebla and the power of Tartessos, but, at the same time, learned much about Atlantic trade from those they conquered. Thus Tartessos became a city of legend to the Greeks and is a candidate, among other places, for the possible site of the Lost Atlantis, or more likely, one of its colonial cities. A rich field for further exploration by competent modern archaeological methods is waiting at the Rio Tinto.

7.

Climax of the Search

Until more specific explorations are made in other parts of the Mediterranean that throw new light on the great Atlantean thalassocracy that controlled the ancient world before 1450 B.C., the most interesting focus of exploration is certainly the island of Thera.

Dr. Anghelos Galanopoulos states it this way: "The description says the Metropolis of Atlantis was a small, sacred island round in shape in the center of which stood a mountainous table-land, which was low on all sides, at a distance of about fifty stades from the sea. [A stade is about one eighth of a mile.] Since this mountain was five stades in diameter, the radius of the island was fifty-two stades, or about 9700 meters, which fits nicely into the dimension of Thera."

The inner harbor of Thera with its burned islands that blew up thousands of years ago has been gradually rebuilding, and the pictures of the growth of the center of the big interior harbor, from the mid-nineteenth century until the more recent eruptions in 1926, show what can happen. Today these burned islands—called New Kaimeni, Palaea Kaimeni, and Micra Kaimeni—tend to become joined again into a new round island where the ancient crater once existed. Smoke comes up from the small fissures, and warm, turgid waters, yellow-green and red, leak out into the clearer blue of the Aegean.

During 1966 and 1967, Dr. Mavor, Professor Galano-poulos, and Professor Marinatos carried on various investigations around the shores of Thera in the harbor and under the overlaying pumice, or *tephra*, near the village of Akrotiri. Thanks to modern science, new electronic devices can search out the shape and the difference in buried objects both underground and undersea. The villages of Thera stand on an outer rim surrounding a central harbor, the old crater, and the newly forming islands rise in the center of this harbor, the whole like a huge jagged tooth with a great central cavity.

This formation, which closely resembles the ancient description of Atlantis, has long intrigued the imaginations of archaeologists. In fact, houses of a Minoan village were unearthed under the pumice almost a hundred years ago when that material was mined on Thera for work on the Suez Canal. As early as the 1930's this was a recognized Minoan site, and it was first suggested then that a great eruption had covered this village, just as Pompeii was later covered and preserved by the ash-fall from Mt. Vesuvius. Professor Marinatos was one of the first archaeologists to ask that this be excavated as

The body of this Pompeiian boy was preserved by the ash fall
from the eruption of Mount Vesuvius in A.D. 79.

a possible source of the Atlantis legend. In 1960 Professor Galanopoulos came to the same conclusion from his studies as a seismologist.

The sea floor around Thera was first sounded with cores, which brought up samples in depth of the bottom, by a Swedish expedition in 1947. The *Vema* of the Lamont Geological Laboratory confirmed the layers of undersea ash and mapped the ocean bottom all around Thera about ten years after the Swedes. In 1965 Dr. Heezen and Dr. Ninkovich analyzed all the evidence and came to the conclusion that the great eruption of Thera had actually taken place about 1450 B.C.

Today we know that a large town covering a half-mile square exists under the *tephra* on the island. Frescoes and oil jars and pieces of furnishings have been recovered, but since no gold or ornaments of any great value have been found, it would seem that the inhabitants were frightened away before the final great explosion. The Greek government plans to go on with the excavations, and more mapping certainly needs to be done on the surrounding sea bottom to identify canals and sea walls that were reported to have existed around the citadel of the ancient Atlantis.

To accomplish this, certain types of skills and the use of modern techniques are required that are unfamiliar to most classical archaeologists. Man cannot as yet work easily two hundred feet underwater in the usual scuba, or in the old-fashioned *mechanicos*, diving equipment for any length of time. But now there do exist machines, cameras, exploring robots, and sunken observation chambers that will soon permit prolonged work and study underwater. Even more important are the electronic shock-recording instruments that not only enable scientists working at sea level to make relief maps of the sea floor, but also to record and analyze these profiles of sediments and underlying rock for the possible existence of buried buildings.

Underwater archaeology began with the aqualung, a device using compressed air fed to the swimmer from a tank strapped to his back. This gave undersea workers much more freedom of movement than the old-fashioned helmet and suit with tubes reaching back to the surface. Jacques-Yves Cousteau and Emile Gagnon first used the aqualung in the early 1940's. It was evident then that if men were to work with both safety and comfort for any length of time undersea at the site of a wreck or a sunken building they must have some refuge for observation over longer periods of time than permitted by the scuba equipment. Most famous of the early models of deep-sea housing that could be let down to the very bottom of the ocean were the successive models of Professor Auguste Piccard's Bathyscaphe. From these pioneer vessels Link and Cousteau built a series of three Conshelf (after Continental Shelf) deep-sea housing units completely equipped for work as far below the surface as the use of aqualungs permitted. During their last exploration in the Mediterranean near Monaco, six men lived in the spherical Conshelf III for almost twenty-two days at a pressure eleven times greater than that of the surface. This experiment proved that an artificial atmosphere of helium and oxygen

A diver off the coast of Turkey brings up a Roman vase from
a ship 150 feet below the surface of the Mediterranean.

helps to remove the danger of narcosis, or nitrogen poisoning, and, further, that housing can be built to harbor workers for depths as low as present scuba techniques permit, which at best is about three hundred feet.

Other such experiments are being carried on by the United States Navy at two-hundred-foot depths off La Jolla, California. And near Honolulu, T. A. Preyer has set up an Oceanographic Institute for the study of undersea living and plans to build an underwater laboratory and workshop along the same lines as the Link-Cousteau Conshelf III.

Small mobile two-men submarine Diving Saucers are used not only to service these undersea housings but for wide explorations along the bottom of the oceans and as workhorses to manipulate and lift objects. One such contrivance called the Alvin, engineered at Woods Hole, was used successfully with two men aboard at a depth of eight hundred and fifty meters off Rota, Spain, in 1966 to help locate and raise the lost hydrogen bomb that fell into the sea there. At present the Alvin can remain in operation under water for from six to eight hours. The Aluminaut and Asherah are similar crafts. Other devices are constantly being developed.

At Thera, however, it is possible that the turgid and colored substances in the water, to say nothing of the heat, may limit the usefulness of these undersea submersibles in the harbor itself. These problems lead to the use of surface ships equipped with an advanced sort of sonar to not only map the profile of the sea bottom, but also to penetrate through sediment and various substances to great depths beneath the sea bottom. Two such instruments are now in use and may well give us the long-sought-after picture of buildings, canals, and vessels buried deep beneath the sea-bottom debris and fallout from the great explosion of 1450 B.C. at Thera.

Profiling the sub-bottom of the sea is done not just by echo from the surface, but also by seismic reflection, that is, an underwater sharp shock of sound penetrates deep into the earth and gives varying echo reflections of the density and volume of substances under the earth. This type of exploration has been tried out by the Woods Hole Oceanographic Institution off Martha's Vineyard, and a profile as much as a mile deep beneath the sea floor has been recorded and analyzed. This requires the use of a computer on the ship as the echoes from the explosions come back from sediment, from stone wall, or rock, all giving their particular signals.

Professor Edgerton of the Massachusetts Institute of Technology has made what he calls a Boomer. A charge of electricity that rams a plate moving at high speed against a heavy bolted resisting plate produces underwater shock. The amount of the electric shock regulates the blow and, hence, the sound wave desired. This machine will be used for further exploration of the sunken and silted-up city of Heliki near Corinth in Greece.

Another machine called a Sparker uses a direct electric arc released underwater causing a strong shock not unlike a miniature lightning stroke. This device has

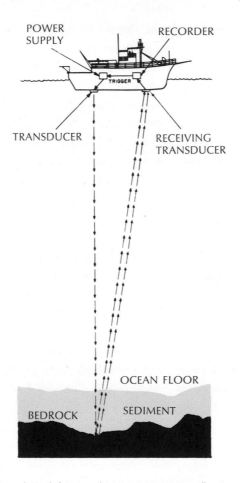

Scientists aboard the vessel interpret seismic reflections to determine the depth and kind of sedimentary layers beneath the sea.

been enlarged by David Caulfield and associates of Mystic Oceanographic Company and was used by Woods Hole in their profile studies off Martha's Vineyard. It has the advantage of a sharper and less diffused echo than the Boomer and seems to give a cleaner profile of what is under the mud at the bottom. Dr. Mavor and Professor Galanopoulos hope to use the Sparker in continuing their explorations in the caldera of Thera.

Through the development of various new devices archaeologists and oceanographers are on the threshold of a great breakthrough in mapping and unveiling the hidden treasures long lost to view on and under the ocean floors of the world. And high time indeed, considering that today more is known about the surface of the moon than about our own ocean bottoms with all they hold of past history and future promise for human welfare. It used to be said, "Go West, young man." Soon it can be, "Get wet, young man, and help discover the marvels of your own new world not lost in space but right at your feet." It might be the Lost Atlantis.

Bibliography

Alsop, Joseph W. *From the Silent Earth: A Report on the Greek Bronze Age.* New York: Harper, 1964.

Bass, George. *Archaeology Under Water.* New York: Praeger, 1966.

Carpenter, Rhys. *The Greeks in Spain.* New York: Longmans, Green and Company, 1925.

Chapin, Henry, and Smith, F. G. Walton. *Ocean River.* New York: Scribners, 1952.

Childe, Gordon. *Piecing Together the Past.* London: Routledge and Paul, 1956.

Childe, Gordon. *What Happened in History.* New York: Penguin, 1946.

Clark, Grahame. *World Prehistory.* Cambridge: Cambridge University Press, 1962.

Cory, M., and Washington, E. H. *Ancient Explorers.* Baltimore: Pelican, 1962.

Daniels, Glyn. *The Idea of Prehistory.* Baltimore: Pelican, 1964.

Dunbabin, T. J. *Western Greeks.* Oxford: Clarendon Press, 1948.

Hutchinson, Richard W. *Prehistoric Crete.* Baltimore: Pelican, 1962.

Lhote, H. *Search for Tassili Frescoes.* New York: Dutton, 1959.

Spence, Lewis. *The History of Atlantis.* London: Rider and Company, 1926.

Velikovsky, Immanuel. *Ages in Chaos.* Garden City, N. Y.: Doubleday, 1952.

Whishaw, E. M. *Atlantis in Andalusia.* London: Rider and Company, 1930.

Index

Man, 30–31
Marinatos, Spyridon, 8, 91–93
Mavor, J. W., Jr., 8, 91, 99
Mayans, 10, 12
Mesopotamia, 27, 35
Micra Kaimeni, 91
Migrations, 10–15, 31–36, 45, 74, 76
Minoans, 38, 44, 45–46, 47–55, 60, 66, 69, 74, 76, 79, 91
Mongols, 14–15
Mummification, 13, 15
Mycenaeans, 19, 23, 39–40, 41, 54, 60, 66, 69, 76, 77, 78
Mystic Oceanographic Company, 99
Myths, see Legends

Nebuchadnezzar, 84
Nestor, 76
New Kaimeni, 91
Niebla, 80, 86–89
Ninkovich, Dragoslav, 59, 93
Noah, 23, 31
Norse sagas, 23
North Africa, 17, 45, 70, 84, 86

Oceanographic exploration, 3, 12–13, 16–17, 25–27, 60, 69, 93–99
Odyssey (Homer), 76–77
Olive trees, 54–55
Orchomenus, 72

Palaea Kaimeni, 91
Pelasgians, 70
Peloponnesus, 7, 66
Pericles, 47
Phaistos, 35, 38, 45, 49, 66, 74
Phocians, 80
Phoenicians, 80, 81, 86, 88–89
Piccard, Auguste, 94
Pirates, 48
Plagues, 72
Plato, 1–7, 8, 10, 46, 47, 66, 68, 80, 81, 86
Pompeii, 91

Pottery, 35, 40, 45, 76, 78
Prehistory, 23–29, 30–31
  methods used, 25
Preyer, T. A., 96
Pylos, 77
Pyramid building, 15

Rhodes, 38
Rice culture, 27
Rio Tinto mines, 88, 89

Sagas, 22–23
  See also Legends
Sahara Desert, 36, 40
Salmon, 13
Sanlucar, 88
Santorini (Thera), 30, 38, 39, 41, 46, 47, 54, 69, 70, 74, 76, 77, 78, 79, 91, 93, 96–97, 99
  the explosion of, 59–68
Schleiman, Heinrich, 19, 23
Seville, 80, 86, 89
Shamanism, 15
Sicily, 48, 81, 84
Solomon, King, 80–81
Solon, 3–6, 35, 47
Solutrians, 15
Spain, 10, 17, 19, 27–28, 36, 45, 47, 80, 87–88
Sparta, 66
Spence, Lewis, 15–16
Stesichorus of Himera, 81, 86
Stone markers, 16
Stronghlie, see Santorini
Sumerians, 27, 31, 34, 84
Syria, 45, 48, 73

Tartessos, 36, 54, 68, 80–87, 89
Tassili, 54
Tenerife, 13
Termier, M., 16
Thebes, 54, 72, 73, 77
Thera, see Santorini
Thutmose III, 72
Tidal waves, 55, 56, 63, 65, 72
Time, 20–29
  chronological, 21